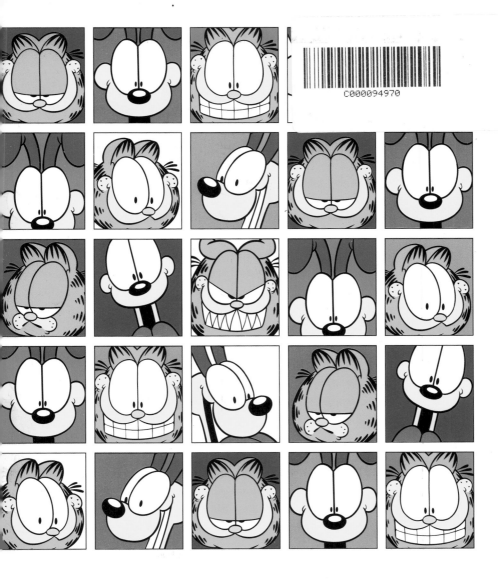

RAVETTE PUBLISHING

First published in 2008 by
Ravette Publishing Ltd
Unit 3, Tristar Centre, Star Road,
Partridge Green, West Sussex RH13 8RA

ISBN: 978-1-84161-307-9

Welcome to Garfield's World!

GARFIELD was born on the comics pages on June 19, 1978. The mastermind of cartoonist Jim Davis, GARFIELD is a humorous strip centred around the lives of a fat, lazy, cynical orange cat who loves lasagna, coffee and his remote control; his owner, the long-suffering John Arbuckle; and Odie, a sweet but dumb dog.

Garfield was introduced to the world in just 41 newspapers but quickly became the fastest growing and **most widely syndicated comic strip ever.** Today **over 200 million readers** see GARFIELD daily in over **2,400 newspapers** around the globe appearing in **63 countries** and translated into **23 languages.**

Over **135 million** Garfield books have been sold worldwide.

Twentieth Century Fox realised the famous fat cat had what it takes to be a movie star, when they invited GARFIELD to appear in his first-ever full-length feature film GARFIELD - THE MOVIE which was released in 2004.

The success of the movie resulted in its release on DVD/VHS. A sequel to the movie, GARFIELD: A TAIL OF TWO KITTIES, was released in 2006 and a DVD/VHS version is currently in the market. Several direct-to-video productions are currently in the making, as is an all-new TV show for kids, The GARFIELD Show, due to debut in 2009.

ASK ME

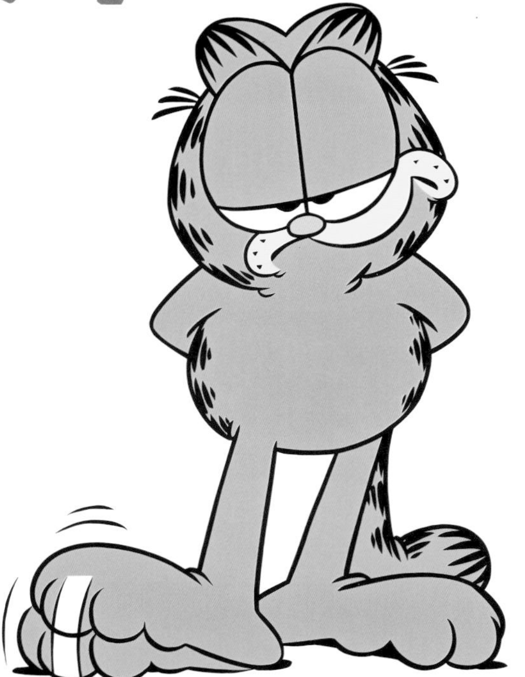

IF I CARE

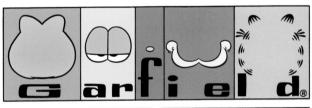

© 1994 PAWS, INC. All Rights Reserved.

JIM DAVIS 7-24

KLACK!

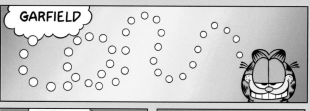

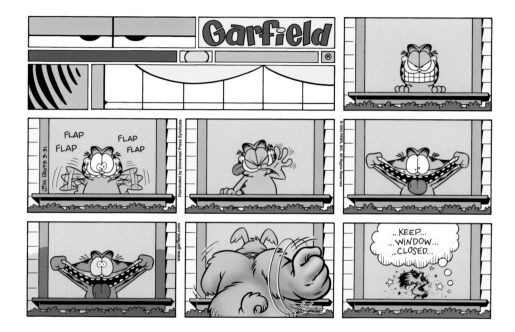

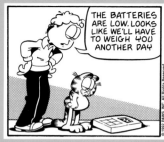

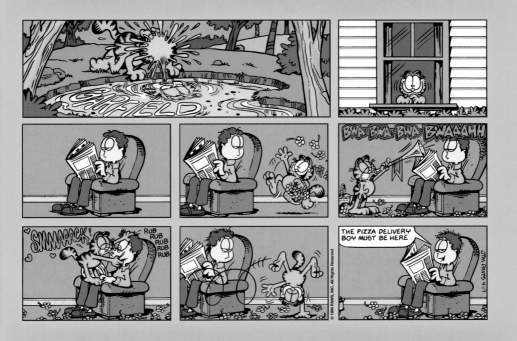

Other GARFIELD Gift Books published by Ravette ...

	ISBN	Price
Gift Books (hardback)		
Don't Know Don't Care	978-1-84161-279-9	£4.99
Get a Grip	978-1-84161-282-9	£4.99
I Don't Do Ordinary	978-1-84161-281-2	£4.99
Keep your attitude, I have my own	978-1-84161-278-2	£4.99
Little Books (paperback)		
C-c-c-caffeine	978-1-84161-183-9	£2.50
Food 'n' Fitness	978-1-84161-145-7	£2.50
Laughs	978-1-84161-146-4	£2.50
Love 'n' Stuff	978-1-84161-147-1	£2.50
Surf 'n' Sun	978-1-84161-186-0	£2.50
The Office	978-1-84161-184-6	£2.50
Zzzzzz	978-1-84161-185-3	£2.50

All Garfield books are available at your local bookshop
or from the publisher at the address below.

Just send your order with your payment and name and address details to:-

RAVETTE PUBLISHING
Unit 3, Tristar Centre
Star Road
Partridge Green
West Sussex RH13 8RA
(tel: 01403 711443 ... email: ravettepub@aol.com)

Prices and availability are subject to change without prior notice.

Please enclose a cheque or postal order made payable to Ravette Publishing
to the value of the cover price of the book and allow the following for UK p&p:-

70p for the first book + 40p for each additional book.